FELIX MENDELSSOHN-BARTHOI‾

SIX CHRISTMAS PIE(

Op.72

Edited by Howard Ferguson

THE ASSOCIATED BOARD OF
THE ROYAL SCHOOLS OF MUSIC

INTRODUCTION

When the 33-year-old Mendelssohn brought his wife to England for the first time in 1842 – it was his own seventh visit – they stayed for six weeks at Denmark Hill in South London with relatives of Frau Mendelssohn named Benecke. During the visit Mendelssohn wrote eight short piano pieces for various members of the family, later revising six of them to form his Op.72. Shortly after his tragically early death on 4 November 1847, the set of pieces was published in two separate editions:

A *Sechs Kinderstücke für das Pianoforte*, Op.72; Breitkopf & Härtel, Leipzig [1847].

B *Six Pieces for the Pianoforte, composed as a Christmas present for his young friends*, Op.72; Ewer, London [1847].

They differ from one another considerably in details of phrasing, and B contains several obviously wrong notes.

The present text is based on A; but since its phrase-marks are very incomplete, the editor has added slurs and staccatos wherever analogy showed that they were undoubtedly intended. Suggested editorial metronome marks have also been added within square brackets at the end of each piece. It should be remembered, however, that they are neither authoritative nor binding. Dynamics within square brackets or crossed with a vertical line are editorial.

Thanks are due to the British Library Board for supplying a microfilm of A; to the Cambridge University Library for allowing access to a copy of B; and to both authorities for giving permission for the use of the material for the present edition.

HOWARD FERGUSON
Cambridge 1982

SIX CHRISTMAS PIECES
Op.72

MENDELSSOHN
1842

Allegro non troppo

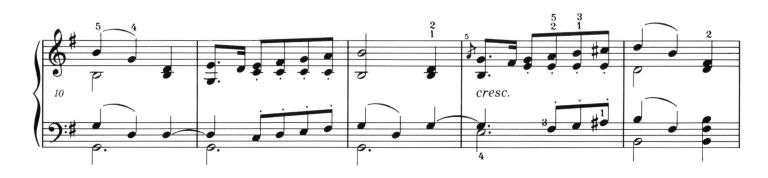

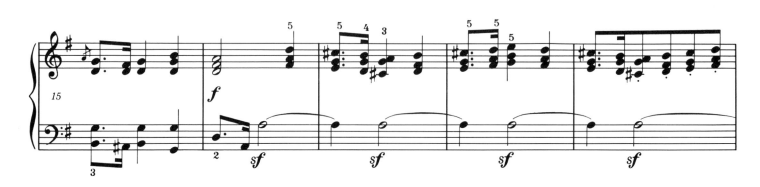

A B 1802

[♩=c.120]

6

[♪ = c. 96]

8

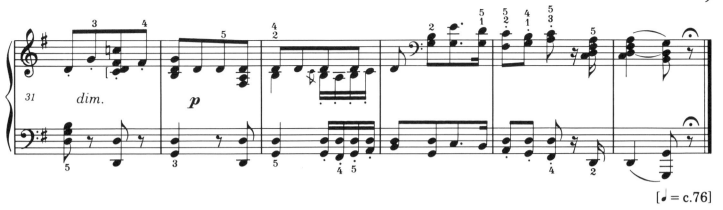

[♩ = c.76]

Andante con moto

[♪. = c. 76]

Allegro assai

[♩ = c. 152]

[♪ = c. 168]